Coco's Bell

Story by Andrew Kelly Illustrations by Julia Crouth

One morning,
Rosie looked out the window
and she saw her cat, Coco.

He had a bird in his paws!

Rosie ran outside into the garden.
"Coco! Let go! Let go!" she cried.

Coco let the bird go,
and jumped away.

But the bird stayed on the grass.

Rosie ran to get the bird.
She went inside with it
and showed her dad.

"Coco got this bird," she said.
"I had to take it away from him.
Its wing looks broken."

Her father went to find a box.
He put an old towel inside it.

Rosie put the bird down
on the towel.

They put some food and water
in the box for the bird.

"I will put the box up here
where Coco can't get it,"
said Dad.

The next morning,
Rosie looked in the box.
The bird was dead.

Rosie was very sad.
"Dad, I love Coco,
but I don't want him to catch
any more birds," she said.
"He will have to stay inside."

"Coco can't stay inside all the time,"
said Dad.
"He has to run around outside.
But we can help the birds.
We can put a little bell on Coco."

"We can go to the shops
and buy one, today," said Rosie.

After that, Coco did not catch any more birds!